CW00556474

Betamonkeys

the evolution of falling

A collection of climbing cartoons
by Ed O'Grady

Betamonkeys

3	Foreword: Tom Randall
5	Introduction: Ed O'Grady
6 - 13	Crag Chat
14 - 19	Products
20 - 25	Guides
26 - 31	People
32 - 37	Speak and Spell
28 - 43	Science
44 - 49	Lightbulb
50 - 56	Wall Talk

The evolution of falling

Foreword

I first met Ed down at The Climbing Station in more of an "observing manner" i.e. I noticed he was always on the prowl, looking at other climbers with great intent. What was he doing I wondered? Was he a talent spotter? As I got chatting and found that he was a psychologist, I presumed to start, that in fact he was making professional observations or something of that sort. Over time though, I got chatting more and more and realised that he was this incredibly observant, funny and self-effacing guy who happened to make cartoons about climbing.

Over the following months, I have to confess I never actually looked out for his work... That quickly became impossible though as everyone around, whether at the wall or on our Facebook pages seemed to be talking about and sharing Ed's cartoons. As I made the transition from "friendly interest" to "hooked" I realised there was an acutely observational aspect to his work. It's really damn good! He hits the nail on the head every time and the type of humour fits in perfectly in the climbing community.
I kind of wish he'd been contributing this stuff to our little world for more time now...!

Tom Randall

As with many things, Betamonkeys is the result of several things all coming together at the same time. I had run a martial arts based webcomic called Mikka Bouzu for about five years. Although it had pockets of popularity worldwide, it never really seemed to spread through the martial arts' community. In the last couple of years of this project, my son was getting more and more serious about climbing and I was getting back into it, having been a keen climber in my younger days.

When the Climbing Station opened in Loughborough everything came together. A real sense of community, pain, frustration, sarcasm and a limitless source of comic material centred on the suffering of all the climbers there. Betamonkeys was born and quickly spread to numbers that still amaze me. Thank you to everyone who has shared and enjoyed the silliness. I hope I have managed to include a few of your favourite cartoons from the last two and a half years in this first collection.

Ed O'Grady

Crag Chat

The crag is where all those months of training pay off. You get to stand around with your mates all failing on the same thing.

I've been getting nowhere for months. I think I need to try something different.

Yeah- have you tried a heel hook on that high sloper?

No- I mean 'something different', like *golf or stamp collecting - or something.

For Shauna

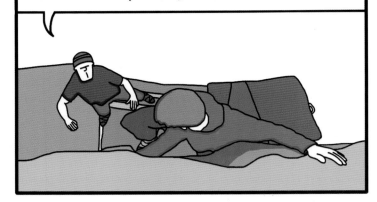

Products

Gear that hasn't seen
the light of day. Yet...

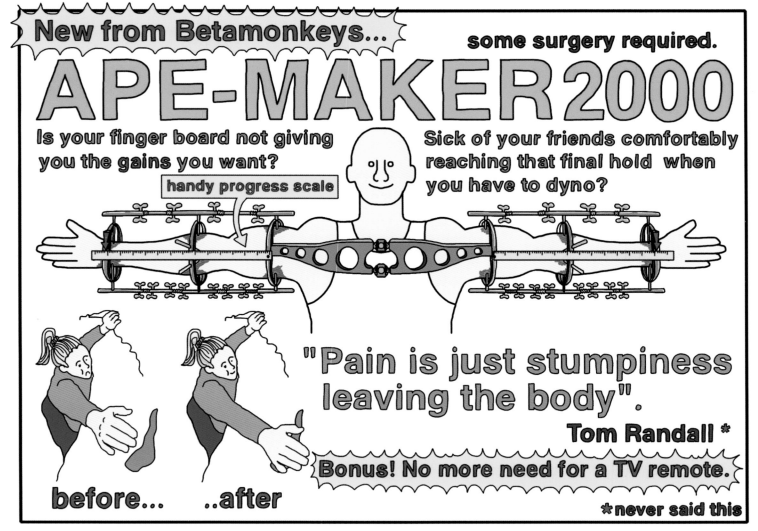

Guides

Guides: used since day one to find the right climb, but not until now to identify the right climbers.

You boulderers think you're so cool with your big chalkbags and silly mattresses and opposable thumbs.

THE BETAMONKEYS' GUIDE TO... CLIMBERS #1 TRAD CLIMBERS

Trad climbers, or 'CLIMBERS' as they prefer to call themselves, distinguish themselves from other styles by the self placement of route protection, rather than relying on pre-placed bolts. They also tend to take their own cutlery to restaurants and would rather use a spontaneously rigged combination of karabiners and a couple of slings, than the more usual 'seatbelt' when driving to a crag, because "pre-placed protection is cheating."

Trad routes are so much harder than other routes that they each requires TWO grades. One for technical difficulty and one for the level of induced terror. This gives trad climbers twice as much to argue about.

Maintaining this level of purity in the ultimate battle of man, or woman, against rock does not come without sacrifice and the trad climber must sacrifice large quantities of cash on the latest in materials technology and cutting edge engineering design that would'nt look out of place on a space station.

Such is the price of keeping it real.

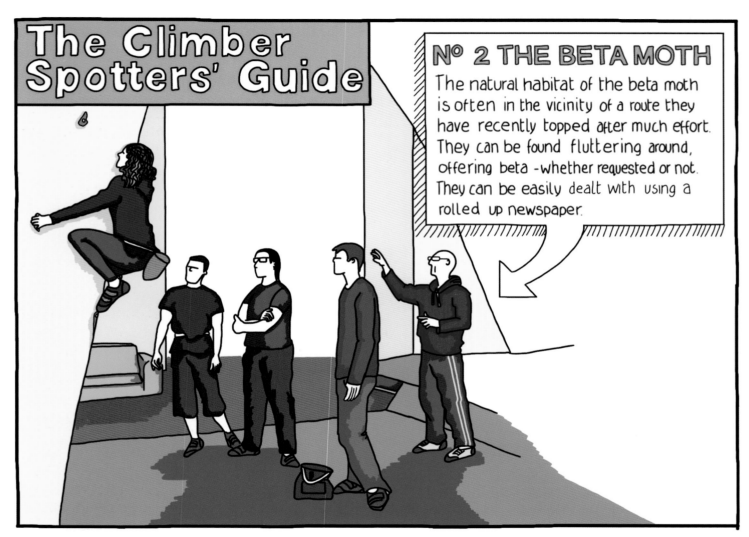

THE BETAMONKEYS' GUIDE TO...
CLIMBERS
#3 THE GRIM BETA

Within any group of climbers there is always one who will provide an apocalyptic guide to whatever route is being attempted. No detail of life threatening horror and the opportunities for personal injury will be excluded, such is their commitment to providing the most thorough route analysis.

Many climbing centres now ban Grim Betas, especially from competition... just in case they are too helpful.

THE BETAMONKEYS' GUIDE TO...
CLIMBING TRIBES

A mainly nomadic people, boulderers carry their bedding with them. Mats are stuffed with their prized, worldly possessions. Many (but never enough) pairs of boots, old jackets, brush sticks (used for pointing and cleaning rituals) and lamps for evening ceremonies. Temporary settlements are known as 'The Project'. These involve sacrifices of human skin and the tribe carry large bags of chalk to use in purification rites and for territorial marking.

All Correct behaviour is governed by 'The Guide', which sets out commandments concerning the 'Proper Route'. The tribal elders will annotate their copies with extra restrictions like 'sit-start', believing it makes them purer. Tribal clothing carries esoteric markings of power and is generally acquired on pilgrimage to obscure foreign sandstone blocs which are "Way better than 'Font!'"

Their bags contain the essentials of extra boots and chalk, at least two more jackets, a variety of whole-food snacks, ethically sourced organic coffee, spare batteries for lamps and rolls of finger tape. They are by no means a primitive tribe and the most 'enlightened ones' use technology to share their wisdom into a collective consciousness called 'The Tubes of You'.

Their dog can climb at least 6b+.

THE BETAMONKEYS' GUIDE TO THE CLIMBER'S CHRISTMAS

BOULDERERS

I think we may have overdone it.

TRAD CLIMBERS

One more on the first pitch, just to be sure.

ICE CLIMBERS

Never mind. The conditions will be better next year.

Pain and Gain

No pain no gain...but what's
the exchange rate...!

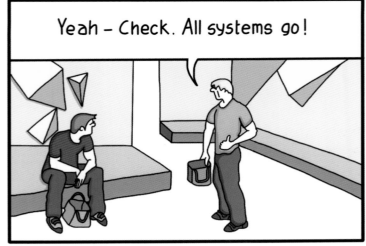

Speak and spell

It's obvious that climbing
has it's own complex vocabulary, yet often it's not what
we say but how we say it
that's crucial...

climber-speak	translation
'That was so close'	You didn't get it
'You were there'	You didn't get it
'You so had it'	You didn't get it
'If you'd just'	You didn't get it
'You've virtually got it'	You didn't get it
'Definitely going to...'	You didn't get it

Some sources suggest that the Sami language may have as many as 180 words for snow. Frankly, this is amateurish when compared to the number of words in the climbers' vocabulary for 'fail'.

Also consider: nearly, almost, next time, soon and project.

Apparently, it's just a little pop up to the sketchy crimp. Then a delicate smear to the finger jam, rock up on that nice pebble. Match your hands on the juggy flake and top out.

THE BETAMONKEYS' GUIDE TO...
CLIMBING TERMINOLOGY

APPARENTLY: I've not actually done it yet but this guy who said he had told me...

POP: Small committed dynamic move.

LITTLE POP: Terrifying leap of faith.

CRIMP: A hand hold so small that it casts no shadow, whatever the time of day.

SKETCHY CRIMP: Imagine the smallest hold you can - then halve it.

SMEAR: there's nothing there so those fancy boots you bought, trust them!

DELICATE: Whatever you do, don't breathe.

JAM: This is what your finger will be turned into if you get it wrong.

PEBBLE: the grain of sand sized hold that sticks out from an otherwise glass wall.

NICE: beautifully polished to dramatically reflect sunlight and have zero friction.

MATCH: It's the only hold.

JUG: A good hand hold.

JUGGY: Not a good hand hold.

FLAKE: you know what that crumbly chocolate does? Well, this is like that.

TOP OUT: drag yourself, walrus like, to relative safety.

Betamonkeys A-Z of Climbing
A is for ARÊTE

The word is thought by many to derive from the French for 'spine' or 'fish bone'. Given the Annoying, fiddly nature of arête climbing, this Makes good sense. However, research from the Linguistics department at the Betamonkeys University suggests that it might have its real roots in an ancient language, meaning 'place where all the good stuff is hidden'. Every climber knows that the good holds are always on the other side of the arête. What we are still unable to explain is how, as you Move around the arête, all the good holds mysteriously move to the side you've just come around from.

The other unexplained aspect of arête physics is that gravity works in two directions. Normal gravity just works in a downward direction, but arête gravity first acts sideways. Only once it has done this does it then drag you off the wall. It is not clear why it does this but it has been suggested that arêtes may have reached a level of consciousness and out of sheer cruelty, want to give you a frustrating glimps of the good holds before throwing you off.

So basically, what you're saying is, be really really strong, be really really flexible, only use the green holds... and don't fall off. Thanks.

Betamonkeys A-Z of Climbing
B is for BETA

The technical guidance for a movement sequence through a crux move or boulder problem. The term is said to originate in a pun referring to the old Betamax video recording format.

Beta is such a complex issue that it has been suggested that it should have its own grading system. Though the complexity would mean that it was virtually useless, the key dimensions are:

Overly detailed ⟺ zen-like vagueness

Patronisingly simplistic ⟺ complexity requiring a PhD in physics

Sarcastically abusive ⟺ Abusively sarcastic

The worst kind of beta is 'retrospective beta'. Every group of climbers has someone specialising in this particular form. They will give a detailed, move by move analysis of what you have just done and why you fell off. Retrospective beta is about as useful as still owning a Betamax video tape and having nothing to play it on.

The first move is the hardest. The next move, that's the hardest too. After that, the difficulty just ramps up all the way to the last move ... And that's just utterly impossible!

Betamonkeys A-Z of Climbing
C is for CRUX

The hardest move on a route. When you've got this, you've pretty much cracked the whole thing. However, as grades have pushed higher, the term has become virtually meaningless. It is therefore not so much a matter of where's the crux?", as of "how 'cruxy' is it?" It is now suggested that careful distinction is made between various types of cruxes.

Opening Crux - The initial pull onto a climb that is so difficult that nothing could be harder... or so you thought.

Pseudo Crux - the move that 'looked' like the crux from the bottom. But with your new found perspective, turns out to be a brief respite from the general awfulness.

Transitional Crux - the nearly impossible move between two genuinely impossible moves.

Über Crux - this is it, it's this one definitely. The actual crux. It has been suggested that über cruxes should themselves be divided into opening, pseudo and transitional cruxes.

Science

Sometimes climbing is all about science; friction, humidity, gravity; most other times blind faith normally works!

How the hell did you get up that!? There is absolutely nothing there!

THE BETAMONKEYS' GUIDE TO SCIENCE.

Recent scientific breakthroughs by researchers in Theoretical Climbing, suggest that as much as 90% of any route consists of **'DARK HOLDS'**. Undetectable with standard methods, like hands, feet and eyes, their existence must be inferred through indirect observation. For example, the fact that others get up routes that you can't.

The research also proposes the existence of **'ANTI-HOLDS'**. Less controversial, these promising looking areas of shadow, ultimately turn out to be just areas of useless discolouration on the rock. It is thought that the boulders of the Peak District have a particularly high concentration of 'anti-holds'.

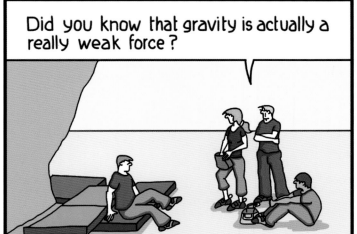

THE BETAMONKEYS' GUIDE TO SCIENCE.
#2 TIME

Newton considered time to be a universal constant. Einstein realised that time was relative. If he had been a climber he would have had much more insight into just how complex the situation is.

We know that time slows down the further you get from home. Added to this, the sheer awesomeness of crags and boulders, further distorts space-time to make time appear to almost stand still. If we add into the equation, the distorting effect of high levels of **BETA ACTIVITY** (which is directly proportional to the number of climbers present), then we can understand why there is always time for 'one more go'.

The number of attempts necessary to complete any given route is, of course,

$$N = n + 1 \quad \text{(where n = number of previous attempts)}$$

So, next time you are late for dinner with the family, that critical job interview or your wedding. Remember, it's not your fault. It's PHYSICS!

THE BETAMONKEYS' GUIDE TO SCIENCE.
THE FIRST LAW OF SMUGNESS

One of the oldest arguments in climbing has finally been put to rest by the Department of Theoretical Climbing at the Betamonkeys' University. How smug is a climber in a group allowed to be once a route has been topped?

$$S_B = \frac{\beta \sqrt{N}}{C} \sum_{i=1}^{N} (V_i^2 A_i) - (V_B^2 A_B)$$

S_B – Allowable level of boulderer smugness.

V_B – Normal usual grade of boulderer in question.

A_B – Number of attempts taken to top route.

V_i – Usual grade of boulderer (i=1-N)

A_i – Number of attempts for boulderer (i=1-N)

C – Number in the group who have previously topped route

N – Number of boulderers in the group.

β – Universall smugness constant (of course it's beta!)

Over 350 million miles ...

.. $2.5 billion dollars ...

.. More hi-tech scientific equipment than you can shake a clip stick at ...

.. But still no sign of intelligent life.

Lightbulb

The best jokes never die, they just hibernate until the next generation pick them up.

HOW MANY CLIMBERS DOES IT TAKE TO CHANGE A LIGHTBULB?

#1 TRAD CLIMBERS: 3 - One to change the bulb, one to belay and one to moan that 'these new light bulbs aren't like the old ones'and 'it's really not been the same since they got rid of gas lamps anyway'.

HOW MANY CLIMBERS DOES IT TAKE TO CHANGE A LIGHTBULB?

#2 BIG WALL CLIMBERS: Just the one. But you'll need a hell of a lot of kit and to be honest, it would probably be quicker to just rewire the whole house.

For Andy K

#3 BOULDERERS :7 (at least) One to change the bulb, one to offer random beta, one in charge of the brush, two spotters, one to check the guide book and one to operate the GoPro®.

HOW MANY CLIMBERS DOES IT TAKE TO CHANGE A LIGHTBULB?

#4 ICE CLIMBERS: 2* But you are going to have to wait for the conditions to be juuuuust right and then redecorate.

*plus any others queuing for their go.

HOW MANY CLIMBERS DOES IT TAKE TO CHANGE A LIGHTBULB?

ROUTE SETTERS Usually 2. But they're going to put it in the most awkward place, it's going to be far *too* small to be of any use and they'll tell you it's energy saving - but it isn't.

Wall Talk

The wall is where we hone our skills. Sneaking Beta, bullsh*tting, wearing super-tight boots and hoovering up excuses.

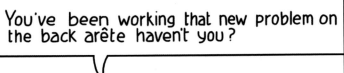

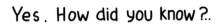